'You el
fowl!'

EDWARD LEAR

Born 1812, Holloway, England

Died 1888, Sanremo, Italy

LEAR IN PENGUIN CLASSICS

The Complete Nonsense and Other Verse

EDWARD LEAR

Nonsense

Illustrations by L. Leslie Brooke

PENGUIN BOOKS

PENGUIN CLASSICS

UK | USA | Canada | Ireland | Australia
India | New Zealand | South Africa

Penguin Classics is part of the Penguin Random House group of companies
whose addresses can be found at global.penguinrandomhouse.com.

This selection first published in Penguin Classics 2016
001

Set in 10/14.5 pt Baskerville 10 Pro
Typeset by Jouve (UK), Milton Keynes
Printed in Great Britain by Clays Ltd, St Ives plc

A CIP catalogue record for this book is available from the British Library

ISBN: 978-0-241-25144-7

www.greenpenguin.co.uk

Penguin Random House is committed to a
sustainable future for our business, our readers
and our planet. This book is made from Forest
Stewardship Council® certified paper.

Contents

The Duck and the
   Kangaroo   1

The Owl and the Pussy-cat   4

The Broom, the Shovel,
   the Poker, and the Tongs   6

Calico Pie   9

The Jumblies   11

The Courtship of the
   Yonghy-Bonghy-Bò   15

The Scroobious Pip   21

The Quangle Wangle's Hat   26

The Akond of Swat   30

The Cummerbund   33

The New Vestments   37

The Two Old Bachelors   41

The Dong with a Luminous
    Nose   46

Some Incidents in the
    Life of my Uncle Arly   51

The Duck and the Kangaroo

Said the Duck to the Kangaroo,
  'Good gracious! how you hop!
Over the fields and the water too,
  As if you never would stop!
My life is a bore in this nasty pond,
And I long to go out in the world beyond!
  I wish I could hop like you!'
  Said the Duck to the Kangaroo.

'Please give me a ride on your back!'
  Said the Duck to the Kangaroo.
'I would sit quite still, and say nothing but
    "Quack,"
  The whole of the long day through!
And we'd go to the Dee, and the Jelly Bo Lee,
Over the land, and over the sea; –
  Please take me a ride! O do!'
  Said the Duck to the Kangaroo.

Said the Kangaroo to the Duck,
  'This requires some little reflection;
Perhaps on the whole it might bring me luck,
  And there seems but one objection,
Which is, if you'll let me speak so bold,
Your feet are unpleasantly wet and cold,
  And would probably give me the roo-
  matiz!' said the Kangaroo.

Said the Duck, 'As I sate on the rocks,
  I have thought over that completely,
And I bought four pairs of worsted socks
  Which fit my web-feet neatly.
And to keep out the cold I've bought a cloak,
And every day a cigar I'll smoke,
  All to follow my own dear true
  Love of a Kangaroo!'

Said the Kangaroo, 'I'm ready!
  All in the moonlight pale;
But to balance me well, dear Duck, sit steady!
  And quite at the end of my tail!'

So away they went with a hop and a bound,
And they hopped the whole world three times round;
   And who so happy, – O who,
   As the Duck and the Kangaroo?

The Owl and the Pussy-cat

The Owl and the Pussy-cat went to sea
   In a beautiful pea-green boat,
They took some honey, and plenty of money,
   Wrapped up in a five-pound note.
The Owl looked up to the stars above,
   And sang to a small guitar,
'O lovely Pussy! O Pussy, my love,
   What a beautiful Pussy you are,
      You are,
      You are!
What a beautiful Pussy you are!'

Pussy said to the Owl, 'You elegant fowl!
   How charmingly sweet you sing!
O let us be married! too long we have tarried:
   But what shall we do for a ring?'
They sailed away, for a year and a day,
   To the land where the Bong-tree grows,

And there in a wood a Piggy-wig stood,
 With a ring at the end of his nose,
  His nose,
  His nose,
With a ring at the end of his nose.

'Dear Pig, are you willing to sell for one shilling
 Your ring?' Said the Piggy, 'I will.'
So they took it away, and were married next day
 By the Turkey who lives on the hill.
They dinèd on mince, and slices of quince,
 Which they ate with a runcible spoon;
And hand in hand, on the edge of the sand,
 They danced by the light of the moon,
  The moon,
  The moon,
They danced by the light of the moon.

The Broom, the Shovel, the Poker, and the Tongs

The Broom and the Shovel, the Poker and Tongs,
    They all took a drive in the Park,
And they each sang a song, Ding-a-dong,
        Ding-a-dong,
    Before they went back in the dark.
Mr Poker he sate quite upright in the coach,
    Mr Tongs made a clatter and clash,
Miss Shovel was dressed all in black (with a
        brooch),
    Mrs Broom was in blue (with a sash).
        Ding-a-dong! Ding-a-dong!
        And they all sang a song!

'Oh Shovely so lovely!' the Poker he sang,
    'You have perfectly conquered my heart!
Ding-a-dong! Ding-a-dong! If you're pleased with
        my song,
    I will feed you with cold apple tart!

When you scrape up the coals with a delicate sound,
　　You enrapture my life with delight!
Your nose is so shiny! your head is so round!
　　And your shape is so slender and bright!
　　　　Ding-a-dong! Ding-a-dong!
　　　　Ain't you pleased with my song?'

'Alas! Mrs Broom!' sighed the Tongs in his song,
　　'O is it because I'm so thin,
And my legs are so long – Ding-a-dong!
　　　　Ding-a-dong!
　　That you don't care about me a pin?
Ah! fairest of creatures, when sweeping the room,
　　Ah! why don't you heed my complaint!
Must you needs be so cruel, you beautiful Broom,
　　Because you are covered with paint?
　　　　Ding-a-dong! Ding-a-dong!
　　　　You are certainly wrong!'

Mrs Broom and Miss Shovel together they sang,
　　'What nonsense you're singing to-day!'
Said the Shovel, 'I'll certainly hit you a bang!'
　　Said the Broom, 'And I'll sweep you away!'

So the Coachman drove homeward as fast as
      he could,
  Perceiving their anger with pain;
But they put on the kettle, and little by little,
  They all became happy again.
    Ding-a-dong! Ding-a-dong!
    There's an end of my song!

Calico Pie

Calico Pie,
 The little birds fly
Down to the calico tree,
 Their wings were blue,
 And they sang 'Tilly-loo!'
 Till away they flew, –
And they never came back to me!
 They never came back!
 They never came back!
They never came back to me!

Calico Jam,
 The little Fish swam,
Over the syllabub sea,
 He took off his hat,
 To the Sole and the Sprat,
 And the Willeby-wat, –

But he never came back to me!
 He never came back!
 He never came back!
He never came back to me!

Calico Ban,
The little Mice ran,
To be ready in time for tea,
Flippity flup,
They drank it all up,
And danced in the cup, –

But they never came back to me!
They never came back!
They never came back!
They never came back to me!

Calico Drum,
The Grasshoppers come,
The Butterfly, Beetle, and Bee,
Over the ground,
Around and round,
With a hop and a bound, –

But they never came back!
They never came back!
They never came back!
They never came back to me!

The Jumblies

They went to sea in a Sieve, they did,
    In a Sieve they went to sea:
In spite of all their friends could say,
On a winter's morn, on a stormy day,
    In a Sieve they went to sea!
And when the Sieve turned round and round,
And every one cried, 'You'll all be drowned!'
They called aloud, 'Our Sieve ain't big,
But we don't care a button! we don't care a fig!
    In a Sieve we'll go to sea!'
        Far and few, far and few,
            Are the lands where the Jumblies live;
            Their heads are green, and their hands are blue,
                And they went to sea in a Sieve.

They sailed away in a Sieve, they did,
    In a Sieve they sailed so fast,
With only a beautiful pea-green veil
Tied with a riband by way of a sail,
    To a small tobacco-pipe mast;
And every one said, who saw them go,

'O won't they be soon upset, you know!
For the sky is dark, and the voyage is long,
And happen what may, it's extremely wrong
    In a Sieve to sail so fast!'
        Far and few, far and few,
            Are the lands where the Jumblies live;
            Their heads are green, and their hands are blue,
                And they went to sea in a Sieve.

The water it soon came in, it did,
    The water it soon came in;
So to keep them dry, they wrapped their feet
In a pinky paper all folded neat,
    And they fastened it down with a pin.
And they passed the night in a crockery-jar,
And each of them said, 'How wise we are!
Though the sky be dark, and the voyage be long,
Yet we never can think we were rash or wrong,
    While round in our Sieve we spin!'
        Far and few, far and few,
            Are the lands where the Jumblies live;
            Their heads are green, and their hands are blue,
                And they went to sea in a Sieve.

And all night long they sailed away;
   And when the sun went down,
They whistled and warbled a moony song
To the echoing sound of a coppery gong,
   In the shade of the mountains brown.
'O Timballo! How happy we are,
When we live in a Sieve and a crockery-jar,
And all night long in the moonlight pale,
We sail away with a pea-green sail,
   In the shade of the mountains brown!'
     Far and few, far and few,
       Are the lands where the Jumblies live;
      Their heads are green, and their hands are blue,
        And they went to sea in a Sieve.

They sailed to the Western Sea, they did,
   To a land all covered with trees,
And they bought an Owl, and a useful Cart,
And a pound of Rice, and a Cranberry Tart,
   And a hive of silvery Bees.
And they bought a Pig, and some green Jack-daws,
And a lovely Monkey with lollipop paws,

And forty bottles of Ring-Bo-Ree,
   And no end of Stilton Cheese.
      Far and few, far and few,
        Are the lands where the Jumblies live;
       Their heads are green, and their hands are blue,
        And they went to sea in a Sieve.

And in twenty years they all came back,
   In twenty years or more,
And every one said, 'How tall they've grown!
For they've been to the Lakes, and the Torrible Zone,
   And the hills of the Chankly Bore!'
And they drank their health, and gave them a feast
Of dumplings made of beautiful yeast;
And every one said, 'If we only live,
We too will go to sea in a Sieve, –
   To the hills of the Chankly Bore!'
      Far and few, far and few,
        Are the lands where the Jumblies live;
       Their heads are green, and their hands are blue,
        And they went to sea in a Sieve.

The Courtship of the Yonghy-Bonghy-Bò

On the Coast of Coromandel
   Where the early pumpkins blow,
    In the middle of the woods
   Lived the Yonghy-Bonghy-Bò.
Two old chairs, and half a candle, –
One old jug without a handle, –
    These were all his worldly goods,
    In the middle of the woods,
    These were all the worldly goods,
   Of the Yonghy-Bonghy-Bò,
   Of the Yonghy-Bonghy-Bò.

Once, among the Bong-trees walking
   Where the early pumpkins blow,
    To a little heap of stones
   Came the Yonghy-Bonghy-Bò.
There he heard a Lady talking,
To some milk-white Hens of Dorking, –
    ''Tis the Lady Jingly Jones!
    On that little heap of stones
    Sits the Lady Jingly Jones!'

Said the Yonghy-Bonghy-Bò,
Said the Yonghy-Bonghy-Bò.

'Lady Jingly! Lady Jingly!
  Sitting where the pumpkins blow,
    Will you come and be my wife?'
  Said the Yonghy-Bonghy-Bò.
'I am tired of living singly, –
On this coast so wild and shingly, –
    I'm a-weary of my life;
    If you'll come and be my wife,
    Quite serene would be my life!' –
  Said the Yonghy-Bonghy-Bò,
  Said the Yonghy-Bonghy-Bò.

'On this Coast of Coromandel,
  Shrimps and watercresses grow,
    Prawns are plentiful and cheap,'
  Said the Yonghy-Bonghy-Bò.
'You shall have my chairs and candle,
And my jug without a handle! –
    Gaze upon the rolling deep
    (Fish is plentiful and cheap;)
    As the sea, my love is deep!'

Said the Yonghy-Bonghy-Bò,
Said the Yonghy-Bonghy-Bò.

Lady Jingly answered sadly,
    And her tears began to flow, –
        'Your proposal comes too late,
    Mr Yonghy-Bonghy-Bò!
I would be your wife most gladly!'
(Here she twirled her fingers madly,)
        'But in England I've a mate!
        Yes! you've asked me far too late,
        For in England I've a mate,
    Mr Yonghy-Bonghy-Bò!
    Mr Yonghy-Bonghy-Bò!'

'Mr Jones – (his name is Handel, –
    Handel Jones, Esquire, & Co.)
        Dorking fowls delights to send,
    Mr Yonghy-Bonghy-Bò!
Keep, oh! keep your chairs and candle,
And your jug without a handle, –
        I can merely be your friend!
        – Should my Jones more Dorkings send,
        I will give you three, my friend!

Mr Yonghy-Bonghy-Bò!
Mr Yonghy-Bonghy-Bò!

'Though you've such a tiny body,
    And your head so large doth grow, –
        Though your hat may blow away,
        Mr Yonghy-Bonghy-Bò!
Though you're such a Hoddy Doddy –
Yet I wished that I could modi-
        fy the words I needs must say!
        Will you please to go away?
        That is all I have to say –
Mr Yonghy-Bonghy-Bò!
Mr Yonghy-Bonghy-Bò!'

Down the slippery slopes of Myrtle,
    Where the early pumpkins blow,
        To the calm and silent sea
    Fled the Yonghy-Bonghy-Bò.
There, beyond the Bay of Gurtle,
Lay a large and lively Turtle; –
        'You're the Cove,' he said, 'for me;
        On your back beyond the sea,
        Turtle, you shall carry me!'

Said the Yonghy-Bonghy-Bò,
Said the Yonghy-Bonghy-Bò.

Through the silent-roaring ocean
  Did the Turtle swiftly go;
    Holding fast upon his shell
  Rode the Yonghy-Bonghy-Bò.
With a sad primæval motion
Towards the sunset isles of Boshen
    Still the Turtle bore him well.
    Holding fast upon his shell,
    'Lady Jingly Jones, farewell!'
  Said the Yonghy-Bonghy-Bò,
  Said the Yonghy-Bonghy-Bò.

From the Coast of Coromandel,
  Did that Lady never go;
    On that heap of stones she mourns
  For the Yonghy-Bonghy-Bò.
On that Coast of Coromandel,
In his jug without a handle,

Still she weeps, and daily moans;
On that little heap of stones
To her Dorking Hens she moans,
For the Yonghy-Bonghy-Bò,
For the Yonghy-Bonghy-Bò.

The Scroobious Pip

The Scroobious Pip went out one day
When the grass was green, and the sky was gray,
Then all the beasts in the world came round
When the Scroobious Pip sate down on the ground.
The Cats and the Dog and the Kangaroo,
The Sheep and the Cow and the Guinea Pig too –
The Wolf he howled, the Horse he neighed,
The little Pig squeaked and the Donkey brayed,
And when the Lion began to roar
There never was heard such a noise before,
And every beast he stood on the tip
Of his toes to look at the Scroobious Pip.

At last they said to the Fox – 'By far
You're the wisest beast – you know you are!
Go close to the Scroobious Pip and say,
"Tell us all about yourself we pray! –
For as yet we can't make out in the least
If you're Fish or Insect, or Bird or Beast."'

The Scroobious Pip looked vaguely round
And sang these words with a rumbling sound –

'Chippetty Flip – Flippetty Chip –
My only name is the Scroobious Pip.'

The Scroobious Pip from the top of a tree
Saw the distant Jellybol$\overline{ee}$, –
And all the birds in the world came there,
Flying in crowds all through the air.
The Vulture and Eagle – the Cock and the Hen,
The Ostrich, the Turkey, the Snipe and Wren,
The Parrot chattered, the Blackbird sung,
And the Owl looked wise but held his tongue,
And when the Peacock began to scream,
The hullabaloo was quite extreme.
And every bird he fluttered the tip
Of his wing as he stared at the Scroobious Pip.

At last they said to the Owl, – 'By far
You're wisest Bird – you know you are!
Fly close to the Scroobious Pip and say,
"Explain all about yourself we pray! –
For as yet we have neither seen nor heard
If you're Fish or Insect, Beast or Bird!"'

The Scroobious Pip looked gaily round
And sang these words with a chirpy sound –

'Flippetty chip – Chippetty flip –
My only name is the Scroobious Pip.'

The Scroobious Pip went into the sea
By the beautiful shore of the Jellybolēe –
All the Fish in the world swam round
With a splashy squashy spluttery sound,
The Sprat, the Herring, the Turbot too,
The Shark, the Sole, and the Mackerel blue,
The —————— spluttered, the Porpoise puffed
——————Flounder ——————————
And when the Whale began to spout –
_____

And every Fish he shook the tip
Of his tail as he gazed on the Scroobious Pip.

At last they said to the Whale – 'By far
You're the biggest Fish – you know you are!
Swim close to the Scroobious Pip and say,
"Tell us all about yourself we pray! –
For to know from yourself is our only wish –
Are you Beast or Insect, Bird or Fish?"'

The Scroobious Pip looked softly round
And sang these words with a liquid sound –

Edward Lear

> 'Plifatty flip – Pliffity flip –
> My only name is the Scroobious Pip.'

The Scroobious Pip sate under a tree
By the silent shores of the Jellybolēē,
All the Insects in all the world
About the Scroobious Pip fluttered and twirled.
Beetles and ——————— with purple eyes
Gnats and buzztilential Flies –
Grasshoppers, Butterflies, Spiders too,
Wasps and Bees and Dragonfly blue,
And when the Gnats began to hum
——————— bounced like a dismal drum –
And every insect curled the tip
Of his snout, and looked at the Scroobious Pip.

At last they said the Ant, – 'By far
You're the wisest Insect – you know you are!
Creep close to the Scroobious Pip and say,
"Tell us all about yourself we pray! –
For we can't find out, and we can't tell why –
If you're Beast or Fish or a Bird or a Fly. –"'

The Scroobious Pip turned quickly round
And sang these words with a whistly sound –

'Wizziby wip – wizziby wip –
My only name is the Scroobious Pip.'

Then all the Beasts that walk on the ground
Danced in a circle round and round,
And all the Birds that fly in the air
Flew round and round in a circle there,
And all the Fish in the Jellybolēe
Swam in a circle about the sea,
And all the Insects that creep or go
Buzzed in a circle to and fro –
And they roared and sang and whistled and cried
Till the noise was heard from side to side –

'Chippetty Tip! Chippetty Tip!
Its only name is the Scroobious Pip.'

The Quangle Wangle's Hat

On the top of the Crumpetty Tree
    The Quangle Wangle sat,
But his face you could not see,
    On account of his Beaver Hat.
For his Hat was a hundred and two feet wide,
With ribbons and bibbons on every side,
And bells, and buttons, and loops, and lace,
So that nobody ever could see the face
            Of the Quangle Wangle Quee.

The Quangle Wangle said
    To himself on the Crumpetty Tree, –
'Jam; and jelly; and bread;
    Are the best of food for me!
But the longer I live on this Crumpetty Tree,
The plainer than ever it seems to me
That very few people come this way
And that life on the whole is far from gay!'
            Said the Quangle Wangle Quee.

But there came to the Crumpetty Tree,
    Mr and Mrs Canary;
And they said, – 'Did ever you see
    Any spot so charmingly airy?
May we build a nest on your lovely Hat?
Mr Quangle Wangle, grant us that!
O please let us come and build a nest
Of whatever material suits you best,
        Mr Quangle Wangle Quee!'

And besides, to the Crumpetty Tree
    Came the Stork, the Duck, and the Owl;
The Snail, and the Bumble-Bee,
    The Frog, and the Fimble Fowl;
(The Fimble Fowl, with a Corkscrew leg;)
And all of them said, – 'We humbly beg,
We may build our homes on your lovely Hat, –
Mr Quangle Wangle, grant us that!
        Mr Quangle Wangle Quee!'

And the Golden Grouse came there,
    And the Pobble who has no toes, –
And the small Olympian bear, –
    And the Dong with a luminous nose.

And the Blue Baboon, who played the flute, –
And the Orient Calf from the Land of Tute, –
And the Attery Squash, and the Bisky Bat, –
All came and built on the lovely Hat
       Of the Quangle Wangle Quee.

And the Quangle Wangle said
  To himself on the Crumpetty Tree, –
'When all these creatures move
  What a wonderful noise there'll be!'
And at night by the light of the Mulberry moon
They danced to the Flute of the Blue Baboon,
On the broad green leaves of the Crumpetty Tree,
And all were as happy as happy could be,
       With the Quangle Wangle Quee.

The Akond of Swat

Who, or why, or which, or *what*, Is the Akond of SWAT?

Is he tall or short, or dark or fair?
Does he sit on a stool or a sofa or chair   or SQUAT,
                                                                   The Akond of Swat?

Is he wise or foolish, young or old?
Does he drink his soup and his coffee cold   or HOT,
                                                                   The Akond of Swat?

Does he sing or whistle, jabber or talk,
And when riding abroad does he gallop or walk   or TROT,
                                                                   The Akond of Swat?

Does he wear a turban, a fez, or a hat?
Does he sleep on a mattress, a bed, or a mat   or a COT,
                                                                   The Akond of Swat?

When he writes a copy in round-hand size,
Does he cross his T's and finish his I's   with a DOT,
                                                                   The Akond of Swat?

Can he write a letter concisely clear
Without a speck or a smudge or a smear   or BLOT,
                                                                   The Akond of Swat?

Do his people like him extremely well?

Or do they, whenever they can, rebel   or PLOT,

           At the Akond of Swat?

If he catches them then, either old or young,

Does he have them chopped in pieces or hung   or SHOT,

           The Akond of Swat?

Do his people prig in the lanes or park?

Or even at times, when days are dark   GAROTTE,

           O the Akond of Swat!

Does he study the wants of his own dominion?

Or doesn't he care for public opinion   a JOT,

           The Akond of Swat?

To amuse his mind do his people show him

Pictures, or anyone's last new poem   or WHAT,

           For the Akond of Swat?

At night if he suddenly screams and wakes,

Do they bring him only a few small cakes   or a LOT,

           For the Akond of Swat?

Does he live on turnips, tea, or tripe?

Does he like his shawl to be marked with a stripe   or a DOT,

           The Akond of Swat?

Does he like to lie on his back in a boat

Like the lady who lived in that isle remote,   SHALOTT,

           The Akond of Swat?

Edward Lear

Is he quiet, or always making a fuss?

Is his steward a Swiss or a Swede or a Russ   or a SCOT,

            The Akond of Swat?

Does he like to sit by the calm blue wave?

Or to sleep and snore in a dark green cave   or a GROTT,

            The Akond of Swat?

Does he drink small beer from a silver jug?

Or a bowl? or a glass? or a cup? or a mug?   or a POT,

            The Akond of Swat?

Does he beat his wife with a gold-topped pipe,

When she lets the gooseberries grow too ripe   or ROT,

            The Akond of Swat?

Does he wear a white tie when he dines with friends,

And tie it neat in a bow with ends   or a KNOT,

            The Akond of Swat?

Does he like new cream, and hate mince-pies?

When he looks at the sun does he wink his eyes   or NOT,

            The Akond of Swat?

Does he teach his subjects to roast and bake?

Does he sail about on an inland lake   in a YACHT,

            The Akond of Swat?

Someone, or nobody, knows I wot

Who or which or why or what   Is the Akond of Swat!

The Cummerbund

AN INDIAN POEM

She sate upon her Dobie,
  To watch the Evening Star,
And all the Punkahs as they passed,
  Cried, 'My! how fair you are!'
Around her bower, with quivering leaves,
  The tall Kamsamahs grew,
And Kitmutgars in wild festoons
  Hung down from Tchokis blue.

Below her home the river rolled
  With soft meloobious sound,
Where golden-finned Chuprassies swam,
  In myriads circling round.
Above, on tallest trees remote,
  Green Ayahs perched alone,
And all night long the Mussak moan'd
  Its melancholy tone.

And where the purple Nullahs threw
  Their branches far and wide, –

The Cummerbund

The silvery Goreewallahs flew
   In silence, side by side, –
The little Bheesties' twittering cry
   Rose on the flagrant air,
And oft the angry Jampan howled
   Deep in his hateful lair.

She sate upon her Dobie, –
   She heard the Nimmak hum, –
When all at once a cry arose, –
   'The Cummerbund is come!'
In vain she fled: – with open jaws
   The angry monster followed,
And so, (before assistance came,)
   That Lady Fair was swollowed.

They sought in vain for even a bone
   Respectfully to bury, –
They said, – 'Hers was a dreadful fate!'
   (And Echo answered 'Very.')
They nailed her Dobie to the wall,
   Where last her form was seen,
And underneath they wrote these words,
   In yellow, blue, and green: –

Edward Lear

'Beware, ye Fair! Ye Fair, beware!
   Nor sit out late at night, –
Lest horrid Cummerbunds should come,
   And swollow you outright.'

The New Vestments

There lived an old man in the Kingdom of Tess,
Who invented a purely original dress;
And when it was perfectly made and complete,
He opened the door, and walked into the street.

By way of a hat, he'd a loaf of Brown Bread,
In the middle of which he inserted his head; –
His Shirt was made up of no end of dead Mice,
The warmth of whose skins was quite fluffy and
    nice; –
His Drawers were of Rabbit-skins; – so were his
    Shoes; –
His Stockings were skins, – but it is not known
    whose; –
His Waistcoat and Trowsers were made of Pork
    Chops; –
His Buttons were Jujubes, and Chocolate Drops; –
His Coat was all Pancakes with Jam for a border,
And a girdle of Biscuits to keep it in order;
And he wore over all, as a screen from bad weather,
A Cloak of green Cabbage-leaves stitched all together.

He had walked a short way, when he heard a
   great noise,
Of all sorts of Beasticles, Birdlings, and Boys; –
And from every long street and dark lane in
   the town
Beasts, Birdles, and Boys in a tumult rushed down.
Two Cows and a Calf ate his Cabbage-leaf Cloak; –
Four Apes seized his Girdle, which vanished
   like smoke; –
Three Kids ate up half of his Pancaky Coat, –
And the tails were devour'd by an ancient He
   Goat; –
An army of Dogs in a twinkling tore *up* his
Pork Waistcoat and Trowsers to give to their
   Puppies; –
And while they were growling, and mumbling
   the Chops,
Ten Boys prigged the Jujubes and Chocolate Drops. –
He tried to run back to his house, but in vain,
For Scores of fat Pigs came again and again; –
They rushed out of stables and hovels and doors, –
They tore off his Stockings, his Shoes, and his
   Drawers; –

And now from the housetops with screechings
   descend,
Striped, spotted, white, black, and gray Cats
   without end,
They jumped on his shoulders and knocked off
   his hat, –
When Crows, Ducks, and Hens made a mincemeat
   of that; –
They speedily flew at this sleeves in a trice,
And utterly tore up his Shirt of dead Mice; –
They swallowed the last of his Shirt with a squall, –
Whereon he ran home with no clothes on at all.

And he said to himself as he bolted the door,
'I will not wear a similar dress any more,
Any more, any more, any more, never more!'

The Two Old Bachelors

Two old Bachelors were living in one house;
One caught a Muffin, the other caught a Mouse.
Said he who caught the Muffin to him who caught
   the Mouse, –
'This happens just in time! For we've nothing in
   the house,
Save a tiny slice of lemon and a teaspoonful of
   honey,
And what to do for dinner – since we haven't any
   money?
And what can we expect if we haven't any dinner,
But to lose our teeth and eyelashes and keep on
   growing thinner?'

Said he who caught the Mouse to him who caught
   the Muffin, –
'We might cook this little Mouse, if we only had
   some Stuffin'!
If we had but Sage and Onion we could do
   extremely well,
But how to get that Stuffin' it is difficult to tell!' –

Those two old Bachelors ran quickly to the town
And asked for Sage and Onions as they wandered
up and down;
They borrowed two large Onions, but no Sage
was to be found
In the Shops, or in the Market, or in all the
Gardens round.

But someone said, – 'A hill there is, a little to
the north,
And to its purpledicular top a narrow way leads
forth; –
And there among the rugged rocks abides an
ancient Sage, –
An earnest Man, who reads all day a most
perplexing page.

'Climb up, and seize him by the toes! – all
studious as he sits, –
And pull him down, – and chop him into endless
little bits!

Then mix him with your Onion, (cut up likewise
    into Scraps,) –
When your Stuffin' will be ready – and very good:
    perhaps.'

Those two old Bachelors without loss of time
The nearly purpledicular crags at once began to
    climb;
And at the top, among the rocks, all seated in a
    nook,
They saw that Sage, a-reading of a most enormous
    book.

'You earnest Sage!' aloud they cried, 'your book
    you've read enough in! –
We wish to chop you into bits to mix you into
    Stuffin'!' –

But that old Sage looked calmly up, and with his
    awful book,
At those two Bachelors' bald heads a certain aim
    he took; –
And over crag and precipice they rolled promiscuous
    down, –

At once they rolled, and never stopped in lane or
    field or town, –

And when they reached their house, they found
    (beside their want of Stuffin')

The Mouse had fled; – and, previously, had eaten
    up the Muffin.

They left their home in silence by the once
    convivial door.

And from that hour those Bachelors were never
    heard of more.

The Dong with a Luminous Nose

When awful darkness and silence reign
  Over the great Gromboolian plain,
    Through the long, long wintry nights; –
When the angry breakers roar
As they beat on the rocky shore; –
    When Storm-clouds brood on the towering
      heights
Of the Hills of the Chankly Bore: –

Then, through the vast and gloomy dark,
There moves what seems a fiery spark,
    A lonely spark with silvery rays
    Piercing the coal-black night, –
    A Meteor strange and bright: –
Hither and thither the vision strays,
    A single lurid light.

Slowly it wanders, – pauses, – creeps, –
Anon it sparkles, – flashes and leaps;
And ever as onward it gleaming goes
A light on the Bong-tree stems it throws.

And those who watch at that midnight hour
From Hall or Terrace, or lofty Tower,
Cry, as the wild light passes along, –
    'The Dong! – the Dong!
    The wandering Dong through the forest goes!
      The Dong! the Dong!
    The Dong with a luminous Nose!'

      Long years ago
    The Dong was happy and gay,
Till he fell in love with a Jumbly Girl
    Who came to those shores one day.
For the Jumblies came in a sieve, they did, –
Landing at eve near the Zemmery Fidd
    Where the Oblong Oysters grow,
    And the rocks are smooth and gray.
And all the woods and the valleys rang
With the Chorus they daily and nightly sang, –
    'Far and few, far and few,
    Are the lands where the Jumblies live;
    Their heads are green, and their hands are blue,
    And they went to sea in a sieve.'

Happily, happily passed those days!
    While the cheerful Jumblies staid;

    They danced in circlets all night long,
     To the plaintive pipe of the lively Dong,
      In moonlight, shine, or shade.
For day and night he was always there
By the side of the Jumbly Girl so fair,
With her sky-blue hands, and her sea-green hair.
Till the morning came of that hateful day
When the Jumblies sailed in their sieve away,
And the Dong was left on the cruel shore
Gazing – gazing for evermore, –
Ever keeping his weary eyes on
That pea-green sail on the far horizon, –
Singing the Jumbly Chorus still
As he sate all day on the grassy hill, –

     'Far and few, far and few,
     Are the lands where the Jumblies live;
     Their heads are green, and their hands are blue,
     And they went to sea in a sieve.'

But when the sun was low in the West,
    The Dong arose and said; –
    – 'What little sense I once possessed
    Has quite gone out of my head!' –
And since that day he wanders still

By lake and forest, marsh and hill,
Singing – 'O somewhere, in valley or plain
Might I find my Jumbly Girl again!
For ever I'll seek by lake and shore
Till I find my Jumbly Girl once more!'

Playing a pipe with silvery squeaks,
Since then his Jumbly Girl he seeks,
And because by night he could not see,
He gathered the bark of the Twangum Tree
On the flowery plain that grows.
And he wove him a wondrous Nose, –
A Nose as strange as a Nose could be!
Of vast proportions and painted red,
And tied with cords to the back of his head.
– In a hollow rounded space it ended
With a luminous Lamp within suspended,
All fenced about
With a bandage stout
To prevent the wind from blowing it out; –
And with holes all round to send the light,
In gleaming rays on the dismal light.

And now each night, and all night long,
Over those plains still roams the Dong;

And above the wail of the Chimp and Snipe
You may hear the squeak of his plaintive pipe
While ever he seeks, but seeks in vain
To meet with his Jumbly Girl again;
Lonely and wild – all night he goes, –
The Dong with a luminous Nose!
And all who watch at the midnight hour,
From Hall or Terrace, or lofty Tower,
Cry, as they trace the Meteor bright,
Moving along through the dreary night, –
     'This is the hour when forth he goes,
     The Dong with a luminous Nose!
     Yonder – over the plain he goes;
          He goes!
          He goes;
     The Dong with a luminous Nose!'

Some Incidents in the Life of my Uncle Arly

O my agèd Uncle Arly! –
Sitting on a heap of Barley
    All the silent hours of night, –
Close beside a leafy thicket: –
On his nose there was a Cricket, –
In his hat a Railway Ticket; –
    (But his shoes were far too tight.)

Long ago, in youth, he squander'd
All his goods away, and wander'd
    To the Timskoop Hills afar.
There, on golden sunsets blazing
Every evening found him gazing, –
Singing, – 'Orb! you're quite amazing!
    How I wonder what you are!'

Like the ancient Medes and Persians,
Always by his own exertions
    He subsisted on those hills; –

Whiles, – by teaching children spelling, –
Or at times by merely yelling, –
Or at intervals by selling
    'Propter's Nicodemus Pills'.

Later, in his morning rambles
He perceived the moving brambles
    Something square and white disclose; –
'Twas a First-class Railway-Ticket
But in stooping down to pick it
Off the ground, – a pea-green Cricket
    Settled on my uncle's Nose.

Never – never more, – oh! never,
Did that Cricket leave him ever, –
    Dawn or evening, day or night; –
Clinging as a constant treasure, –
Chirping with a cheerious measure, –
Wholly to my uncle's pleasure, –
    (Though his shoes were far too tight.)

So, for three-and-forty winters,
Till his shoes were worn to splinters,
    All those hills he wander'd o'er, –
Sometimes silent; – sometimes yelling; –

Till he came to Borly-Melling,
Near his old ancestral dwelling; –
　　– And he wander'd thence no more.

On a little heap of Barley
Died my agèd Uncle Arly,
　　And they buried him one night; –
Close beside the leafy thicket; –
There, – his hat and Railway Ticket; –
There, – his ever faithful Cricket; –
　　(But his shoes were far too tight.)

1. BOCCACCIO · *Mrs Rosie and the Priest*
2. GERARD MANLEY HOPKINS · *As kingfishers catch fire*
3. *The Saga of Gunnlaug Serpent-tongue*
4. THOMAS DE QUINCEY · *On Murder Considered as One of the Fine Arts*
5. FRIEDRICH NIETZSCHE · *Aphorisms on Love and Hate*
6. JOHN RUSKIN · *Traffic*
7. PU SONGLING · *Wailing Ghosts*
8. JONATHAN SWIFT · *A Modest Proposal*
9. *Three Tang Dynasty Poets*
10. WALT WHITMAN · *On the Beach at Night Alone*
11. KENKŌ · *A Cup of Sake Beneath the Cherry Trees*
12. BALTASAR GRACIÁN · *How to Use Your Enemies*
13. JOHN KEATS · *The Eve of St Agnes*
14. THOMAS HARDY · *Woman much missed*
15. GUY DE MAUPASSANT · *Femme Fatale*
16. MARCO POLO · *Travels in the Land of Serpents and Pearls*
17. SUETONIUS · *Caligula*
18. APOLLONIUS OF RHODES · *Jason and Medea*
19. ROBERT LOUIS STEVENSON · *Olalla*
20. KARL MARX AND FRIEDRICH ENGELS · *The Communist Manifesto*
21. PETRONIUS · *Trimalchio's Feast*
22. JOHANN PETER HEBEL · *How a Ghastly Story Was Brought to Light by a Common or Garden Butcher's Dog*
23. HANS CHRISTIAN ANDERSEN · *The Tinder Box*
24. RUDYARD KIPLING · *The Gate of the Hundred Sorrows*
25. DANTE · *Circles of Hell*
26. HENRY MAYHEW · *Of Street Piemen*
27. HAFEZ · *The nightingales are drunk*
28. GEOFFREY CHAUCER · *The Wife of Bath*
29. MICHEL DE MONTAIGNE · *How We Weep and Laugh at the Same Thing*
30. THOMAS NASHE · *The Terrors of the Night*
31. EDGAR ALLAN POE · *The Tell-Tale Heart*
32. MARY KINGSLEY · *A Hippo Banquet*
33. JANE AUSTEN · *The Beautifull Cassandra*
34. ANTON CHEKHOV · *Gooseberries*
35. SAMUEL TAYLOR COLERIDGE · *Well, they are gone, and here must I remain*
36. JOHANN WOLFGANG VON GOETHE · *Sketchy, Doubtful, Incomplete Jottings*
37. CHARLES DICKENS · *The Great Winglebury Duel*
38. HERMAN MELVILLE · *The Maldive Shark*
39. ELIZABETH GASKELL · *The Old Nurse's Story*
40. NIKOLAY LESKOV · *The Steel Flea*

41. HONORÉ DE BALZAC · *The Atheist's Mass*
42. CHARLOTTE PERKINS GILMAN · *The Yellow Wall-Paper*
43. C. P. CAVAFY · *Remember, Body . . .*
44. FYODOR DOSTOEVSKY · *The Meek One*
45. GUSTAVE FLAUBERT · *A Simple Heart*
46. NIKOLAI GOGOL · *The Nose*
47. SAMUEL PEPYS · *The Great Fire of London*
48. EDITH WHARTON · *The Reckoning*
49. HENRY JAMES · *The Figure in the Carpet*
50. WILFRED OWEN · *Anthem For Doomed Youth*
51. WOLFGANG AMADEUS MOZART · *My Dearest Father*
52. PLATO · *Socrates' Defence*
53. CHRISTINA ROSSETTI · *Goblin Market*
54. *Sindbad the Sailor*
55. SOPHOCLES · *Antigone*
56. RYŪNOSUKE AKUTAGAWA · *The Life of a Stupid Man*
57. LEO TOLSTOY · *How Much Land Does A Man Need?*
58. GIORGIO VASARI · *Leonardo da Vinci*
59. OSCAR WILDE · *Lord Arthur Savile's Crime*
60. SHEN FU · *The Old Man of the Moon*
61. AESOP · *The Dolphins, the Whales and the Gudgeon*
62. MATSUO BASHŌ · *Lips too Chilled*
63. EMILY BRONTË · *The Night is Darkening Round Me*
64. JOSEPH CONRAD · *To-morrow*
65. RICHARD HAKLUYT · *The Voyage of Sir Francis Drake Around the Whole Globe*
66. KATE CHOPIN · *A Pair of Silk Stockings*
67. CHARLES DARWIN · *It was snowing butterflies*
68. BROTHERS GRIMM · *The Robber Bridegroom*
69. CATULLUS · *I Hate and I Love*
70. HOMER · *Circe and the Cyclops*
71. D. H. LAWRENCE · *Il Duro*
72. KATHERINE MANSFIELD · *Miss Brill*
73. OVID · *The Fall of Icarus*
74. SAPPHO · *Come Close*
75. IVAN TURGENEV · *Kasyan from the Beautiful Lands*
76. VIRGIL · *O Cruel Alexis*
77. H. G. WELLS · *A Slip under the Microscope*
78. HERODOTUS · *The Madness of Cambyses*
79. *Speaking of Siva*
80. *The Dhammapada*

81. JANE AUSTEN · *Lady Susan*

82. JEAN-JACQUES ROSSEAU · *The Body Politic*

83. JEAN DE LA FONTAINE · *The World is Full of Foolish Men*

84. H. G. WELLS · *The Sea Raiders*

85. LIVY · *Hannibal*

86. CHARLES DICKENS · *To Be Read at Dusk*

87. LEO TOLSTOY · *The Death of Ivan Ilyich*

88. MARK TWAIN · *The Stolen White Elephant*

89. WILLIAM BLAKE · *Tyger, Tyger*

90. SHERIDAN LE FANU · *Green Tea*

91. *The Yellow Book*

92. OLAUDAH EQUIANO · *Kidnapped*

93. EDGAR ALLAN POE · *A Modern Detective*

94. *The Suffragettes*

95. MARGERY KEMPE · *How To Be a Medieval Woman*

96. JOSEPH CONRAD · *Typhoon*

97. GIACOMO CASANOVA · *The Nun of Murano*

98. W. B. YEATS · *A terrible beauty is born*

99. THOMAS HARDY · *The Withered Arm*

100. EDWARD LEAR · *Nonsense*

101. ARISTOPHANES · *The Frogs*

102. FRIEDRICH NIETZSCHE · *Why I Am so Clever*

103. RAINER MARIA RILKE · *Letters to a Young Poet*

104. LEONID ANDREYEV · *Seven Hanged*

105. APHRA BEHN · *Oroonoko*

106. LEWIS CARROLL · *O frabjous day!*

107. JOHN GAY · *Trivia: or, the Art of Walking the Streets of London*

108. E. T. A. HOFFMANN · *The Sandman*

109. DANTE · *Love that moves the sun and other stars*

110. ALEXANDER PUSHKIN · *The Queen of Spades*

111. ANTON CHEKHOV · *A Nervous Breakdown*

112. KAKUZO OKAKURA · *The Book of Tea*

113. WILLIAM SHAKESPEARE · *Is this a dagger which I see before me?*

114. EMILY DICKINSON · *My life had stood a loaded gun*

115. LONGUS · *Daphnis and Chloe*

116. MARY SHELLEY · *Matilda*

117. GEORGE ELIOT · *The Lifted Veil*

118. FYODOR DOSTOYEVSKY · *White Nights*

119. OSCAR WILDE · *Only Dull People Are Brilliant at Breakfast*

120. VIRGINIA WOOLF · *Flush*

121. ARTHUR CONAN DOYLE · *Lot No. 249*

122. *The Rule of Benedict*
123. WASHINGTON IRVING · *Rip Van Winkle*
124. *Anecdotes of the Cynics*
125. VICTOR HUGO · *Waterloo*
126. CHARLOTTE BRONTË · *Stancliffe's Hotel*